THE OPTIMISTIC SEED
A STORY OF RESILIENCE

BY
KEVIN KITRELL ROSS
ILLUSTRATION BY HALLINSON PULIDO

MYND MATTERS

This is a work of fiction. Any resemblance to actual events or persons, living or dead, is entirely coincidental.

Books may be purchased in quantity and/or special sales by contacting the publisher.

Mynd Matters Publishing
715 Peachtree Street NE
Suites 100 & 200
Atlanta, GA 30308
www.myndmatterspublishing.com

978-1-953307-01-9

FIRST EDITION

DEDICATION:

HER ALTO VOICE WOULD SING A SONG
WHILE READING MY BEDTIME TALES.

FROM GOLDILOCKS AND DR. SEUSS,
TO MAGIC FROGS AND BOATS WITH SAILS.

HER NEEDLEPOINT HANDS TURNED THE PAGE
OF STORIES OLD AND NEW.
OF KNIGHTS AND LORDS AND DRAGONS,
AND SOJOURNER TRUTH.

FROM MAGIC IN OCTOBER,
AND MIRACLES ON CHRISTMAS EVE,
HER WORDS SPUN WORLDS OF WONDER.
HER WORDS MADE ME BELIEVE.

THAT ONE DAY I COULD WRITE A TALE
ONE THAT SHE WOULD READ,
TO GIRLS AND BOYS AT SLEEPY TIME
TO SWEETEN UP THEIR DREAMS.

SO WHO'S THE SHE THAT I SPEAK OF
THAT SPUN MY WORLD OF DREAMS?
MY MOM, OF COURSE,
MS. JANICE ROSS,
THE SECRET OF THE SEED.

ONCE THERE WAS A SEED,
CARRIED BY THE WIND,
UPON UNFRIENDLY LANDS
THAT REFUSED TO LET IT IN.

YET OVER TIME, WITH STEADY GRIND,
WITHOUT FUSS OR ARGUMENT,
THE SEARCHING SEED DID SUCCEED
AND FOUND A PLACE TO NEST.

FOR DARING ROOTS THAT PRESSED A PATH
OF STONE AND SAND, THEN CLAY,
WORKED IN THE DARK AND THEN IN LIGHT,
ROOTING NIGHT AND DAY.

NO EARTHEN PREDATOR ITS FOE,
NOR SCORCHING HEAT DOTH MAIM,
THIS CREATURE OF UNYIELDING FAITH
TREATED EVERY INCH THE SAME.

FOR DEEP WITHIN THIS STUBBORN SEED,
A SECRET HAD BEEN TOLD.
A SECRET WHICH IT DID RECEIVE,
EMBEDDED ON ITS SOUL.

IT NEVER KNEW IT COULDN'T.
NEVER TOLD IT SHOULD NOT TRY.
WAS NEVER MADE TO FEAR THE WIND.
IN FACT, WAS DARED TO FLY.

AND FLY IT DID,
THROUGH DISTANT WINDS,
AND LANDED ON ITS OWN.
ITS IGNORANCE—YEA, INNOCENCE,
BRAVED AND MADE ITSELF A HOME.

THE COARSE AND UNFIT TERRAIN,
THE DENSE AND CALLOUS SCENE,
HAD NO EFFECT TO REJECT
THE OPTIMISTIC SEED.

FOR WET WAS FOUND
DEEP IN THE GROUND
THAT QUENCHED ITS LONGING THIRST,
FOR JUST THE SCENT
IT WOULD NOT RELENT
OR ALTER ITS NEWFOUND COURSE.

DOWN THE ANCIENT PATH IT WENT,
GRASPING THE SEDIMENT.
AND WITH ITS LINES,
IT GREW WISE,
YET WOULD SOON FORGET.

THE RIGORS OF BURROWING
IN CONCRETE AND IN COLD;
THE BLISTERS IT WAS CARRYING
FROM SCRAPING AGAINST THE ROAD.

BUT WHAT IT COULD REMEMBER,
WHAT IT DID ACCOUNT,
SPUN SILKY ROOTS TO TIMBER,
TURNED SEED STUFF INTO MOUNT.

14

AND MOUNT IT DID,
AN UPWARD CLIMB
ON PATHS IT ONCE DID STOKE.
AND HUNGERING FOR LIGHT AND SKY,
THE SEEDLING TURNED TO OAK.

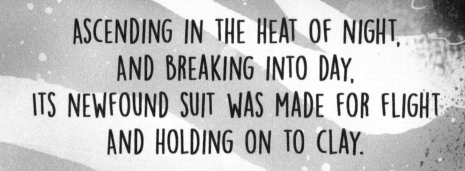

ASCENDING IN THE HEAT OF NIGHT,
AND BREAKING INTO DAY,
ITS NEWFOUND SUIT WAS MADE FOR FLIGHT
AND HOLDING ON TO CLAY.

THEN, STRETCH IT DID,
PAST ALPINES' HEIGHTS,
THROUGH AIRY CLOUDS,
AND STARRY NIGHTS.

THERE, RESTED IN THE OPEN DAY,
A FULL—GROWN MAMMOTH TREE,
OF SOLID TRUNK
AND MAJESTIC BRANCH
AND CLEAR IDENTITY.

A FORCE WITHIN THE FOREST,
A SIGHT THAT COULDN'T BE UNSEEN,
THE ENVY OF THE FLORIST
WAS FAMED AMONG THE TREES.

JOHNATHAN
LIVINGSTON
SEAGULL

A SIMPLE WORD
ASKED THE BIRD
OF HOW IT CAME TO BE.
THE OAK THEN SPOKE,
AND DID INVOKE
THE SECRET OF THE SEED.

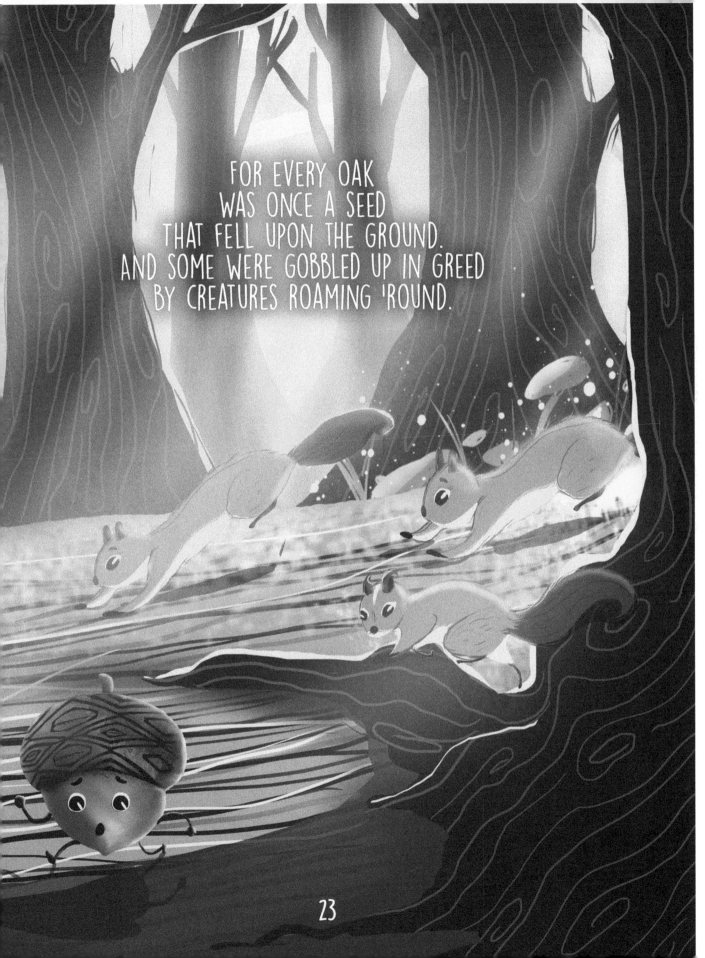

FOR EVERY OAK
WAS ONCE A SEED
THAT FELL UPON THE GROUND.
AND SOME WERE GOBBLED UP IN GREED
BY CREATURES ROAMING 'ROUND.

AND THERE WAS I,
BENEATH THE SKY,
GAZING THROUGH THE LEAVES,
AND CAUGHT THE SIGHT
OF RAVEN'S FLIGHT
AND THERE GAVE BIRTH
MY DREAM.

TO TOUCH THE SKY,
TO KISS THE STARS,
TO PERCH THE LOFTY CLOUDS.

TO GREET THE SUN,
TO GRASP THE MOON,
TO PEER ABOVE THE CROWDS.

25

AND THEN AND THERE,
A FRIENDLY VOICE
SPOKE WITH CLARITY;
PROPHESIED THROUGH WHISPERED WORDS
A SIMPLE TRUTH TO ME.

26

YOU WILL GREET THE SUN EACH DAY,
AND KISS THE SKIES ABOVE.
YOU WILL HUG THE RAINBOWS
AND LIVE A LIFE YOU LOVE.

YOU WILL GRASP THE MOON EACH NIGHT
AND TOWER AMONG THE TREES."

THE SECRET OF MY SOUL WAS SHOWN IF ONLY I BELIEVE.

'BELIEVED IN WHAT?'
I DARED TO ASK
THE VOICE THAT SPOKE TO ME.

'YOURSELF, OF COURSE.
IT IS YOUR CHOICE,
THESE SKIES BELONG TO THEE.

FOR FROM THE START,
WITHIN YOUR HEART,
FOR HEIGHTS YOU ONCE DID DREAM.

YOU WRESTLED WITH YOURSELF, DEAR SEED,
FOR OAK, YOU WERE INDEED

BORN TO HOST
THE WINGED ONES,
THEIR DENS
YOU WOULD RECEIVE.

YOUR SECRET POWER
FOR WHY YOU TOWER
IS KNOWN AMONG THE TREES.

31

YOU BELIEVED, ACORN,
WHAT WAS FORETOLD
FOR COUNTLESS CENTURIES.

TO SEEDS LIKE YOU
WHO SELDOM DO
ROOT BENEATH THE BREEZE.

YOU CLAIMED YOUR GROUND,
YOU EARNED YOUR CROWN,
A GIANT TO BE SEEN.

YOU CAN'T PLAY SMALL.
YOU NOW STAND TALL.
FOR YOU WERE
BORN WORTHY!'"

ABOUT THE AUTHOR

KEVIN KITRELL ROSS, AFFECTIONATELY KNOWN AS "REV. KEV," IS A SOUTHSIDE CHICAGO NATIVE, MOREHOUSE MAN, AND ORDAINED UNITY MINISTER. HE IS A RESPECTED SOCIAL JUSTICE ACTIVIST AND COMMUNITY LEADER COMMITTED TO DISMANTLING SYSTEMIC RACISM AND BUILDING DR. KING'S BELOVED COMMUNITY. HE IS AN AWARD—WINNING HUMANITARIAN RECOGNIZED FOR HIS NUMEROUS MENTORING AND EARLY—COLLEGE EXPOSURE CAMPS THAT SERVE AMERICA'S INNER—CITY YOUTH.

REV. KEV IS THE CREATOR OF "KHAVON MARTIN," A CHILDREN'S SOCIAL MEDIA CHARACTER THAT ENTERTAINS AND EMPOWERS YOUTH WITH TOOLS FOR ADDRESSING RACE—BASED TRAUMA AND THE COMPLEXITIES OF GROWING UP IN DIFFICULT TIMES. HE HAS BEEN PROFILED AND INTERVIEWED IN NATIONAL MAGAZINES, NEWSPAPERS, BLOGS AND TELEVISION—INCLUDING APPEARING TWICE ON OPRAH. AMONG HIS GREATEST HONORS WAS BEING AN INVITED GUEST TO OPEN A SESSION OF THE UNITED STATES CONGRESS WITH A PRAYER FOR THE NATION.

REV. KEV RESIDES IN SACRAMENTO, CALIFORNIA WITH HIS WIFE AND THREE CHILDREN, WHERE HE SERVES AS THE SENIOR MINISTER OF UNITY OF SACRAMENTO INTERNATIONAL SPIRITUAL CENTER.

CPSIA information can be obtained
at www.ICGtesting.com
Printed in the USA
BVHW062124300920
590046BV00001B/7